Stars in the sky

I am Princess Plus.
I am from the Planet Add.
This is a plus sign:
Add when you see it.

Add the stars.
Find the answer.

A.

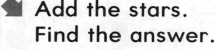

5 + 2 = ☐

B.

3 + 3 = ☐

C.

4 + 1 = ☐

D.

6 + 3 = ☐

1

Space creatures

altogether
in all
total
sum

These words help us to know when to add.

This is a number sentence: ___7___ + ___6___ = 13

Write a number sentence for each problem.
Find the answer. Read it to someone.

A.

6 creatures came.

4 more came.
How many altogether?

____ + ____ = ☐

B.

9 creatures walked in.

2 more walked in.
Find the sum.

____ + ____ = ☐

C.

5 creatures flew down.

3 more flew down.
How many in all?

____ + ____ = ☐

D.

7 creatures landed.

8 more landed.
Find the total.

____ + ____ = ☐

In orbit

Remember: + means add.
Another word that means
to add is "both".

Find the answer.

A.

8 astronauts went into orbit.

2 went into another orbit.

10

How many in both orbits? ☐

B.

6 helmets were on a table.

5 more were on another table.

How many helmets were on both tables? ☐

C.

9 stars came out.

3 more came out.

How many were there altogether? ☐

D.

9 planets were found.

7 more were found.

Find the sum. ☐

E.

8 comets were in orbit.

6 more went into orbit.

Find the total in orbit. ☐

F.

9 moons went around one planet.

9 more went around another planet.

How many went around both planets? ☐

On the moon

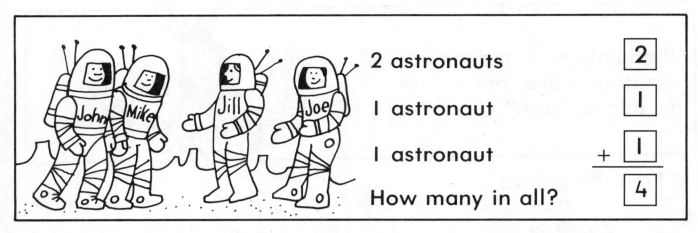

2 astronauts   `2`

1 astronaut   `1`

1 astronaut   + `1`

How many in all?   `4`

◀ Write the numbers. Add the numbers. Write the answer.

A.

John made 1 trip.   ☐

He made 2 more trips.   ☐

Then he made 3 more.   + ☐

How many in all?   ☐

B.

Jill found 5 rocks.   ☐

She found 3 more.   ☐

Then she found 4 more.   + ☐

Find the sum.   ☐

C.

Mike saw 3 creatures. He saw 4 more.   ☐ ☐

Then he saw 6 more.   + ☐

How many altogether?   ☐

D.

Joe saw 2 footprints.   ☐

He saw 6 more.   ☐

Then he saw 8 more.   + ☐

Find the total.   ☐

King Minus

I am King Minus.
I am from the Planet Subtract.
I like to "take away" things.
This is a minus sign: ▭
It means to subtract.

"How many are left?" means to subtract.

◀ Write a number sentence for each problem.
Find the answer.

A.

How many are left?

___6___ – ___2___ = ⃞ 4 ⃞

B.

How many are left?

_____ – _____ = ⃞

C.

How many are left?

_____ – _____ = ⃞

5

Rockets in space

"How many more?" also means to subtract.

Whenever I compare, I subtract.

When I subtract, I take away.

The Blue Star had 10 planets.
The Pink Star had 7 planets.
How many more planets did the Blue Star have?

$\underline{10} - \underline{7} = \boxed{3}$

Find the answer.

A.

The  is 10 feet tall.

The  is 6 feet tall.

How much taller is the  ?

$10 - 6 = \boxed{}$

B.

The  had 6 children in it.

The had 5 children.

How many more children on the  ?

$6 - 5 = \boxed{}$

C.

The  went to 8 planets.

The went to 4 planets.

How many more planets did the go to?

$\underline{} - \underline{} = \boxed{}$

D.

The made 9 trips.

The made 2 trips.

How many more trips did the make?

$\underline{} - \underline{} = \boxed{}$

Creature chase

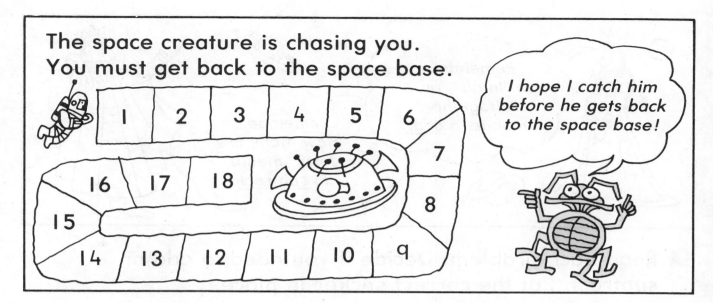

The space creature is chasing you.
You must get back to the space base.

I hope I catch him before he gets back to the space base!

Write the missing numbers.

A.

You are on step 1.
How many more steps to get to 3?

$1 + \boxed{} = 3$

B.

The creature is on step 2.
You are on step 3.
How far ahead are you?

$2 + \boxed{} = 3$

C.

The creature is on step 3.
You are on step 6.
How far ahead are you?

$\boxed{} + \boxed{} = \boxed{}$

D.

You are on step 7.
How many more steps to get to 11?

$\boxed{} + \boxed{} = \boxed{}$

E.

The creature is on step 7.
You are on step 13.
How far ahead are you?

$\boxed{} + \boxed{} = \boxed{}$

F.

You are on step 14.
How many more steps to get to 18?

$\boxed{} + \boxed{} = \boxed{}$

You are safe!

Space caper

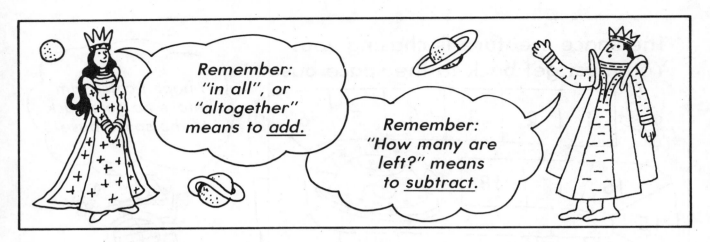

Remember: "in all", or "altogether" means to *add.*

Remember: "How many are left?" means to *subtract.*

Read each problem. Decide if you need to add or subtract. Put the correct sticker in place.
Find the answer.

A.

 3 creatures took off.

2 more took off.
How many altogether?

3 (sticker) 2 =

B.

8  spaceships landed.

5 flew away.
How many were left?

8 (sticker) 5 =

C.

q  space buggies came.

4 went away.
How many were left?

q (sticker) 4 =

D.

7  astronauts went into space.

6 more went into space.
How many in all?

7 (sticker) 6 =

Make a rocket ship

Read each problem. Decide whether you need to add or subtract. Find the answer. Then find the sticker with the matching answer. Put it in place.

sticker

A.

The Great Red Star has 9 planets.
The Big Blue Star has 4 planets.
How many more planets does the Great Red Star have?

sticker

B.

6 rockets took off.
3 came back home.
How many were <u>still</u> gone?

sticker

C.

9 comets passed by the star.
6 more comets passed by the star.
What is the total number of comets?

sticker

D.

It takes 18 hours to get to the Green Planet.
The rocket has travelled 9 hours.
How many hours are left in the trip?

Earth money

Princess Plus is planning a trip to Earth. But first she needs to learn about money on Earth!

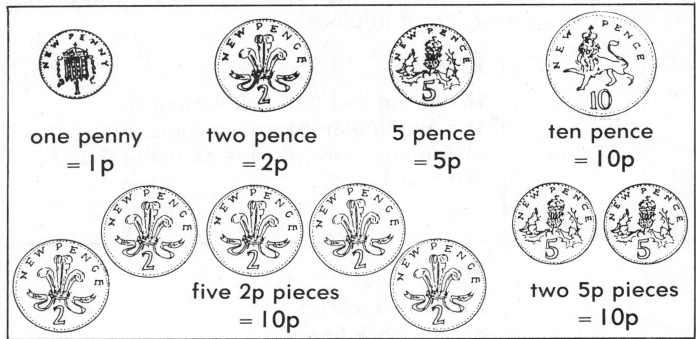

one penny = 1p

two pence = 2p

5 pence = 5p

ten pence = 10p

five 2p pieces = 10p

two 5p pieces = 10p

Find the answer.

A. You have 10 pence.
You get 7 pence.
How many pence do you have altogether?

$$\begin{array}{r} 10 \\ +\ 7 \\ \hline 17 \end{array}$$

B. You have 4 pence.
You get 10 pence.
How many pence do you have in all?

C. You have a 5p piece.
You get a 10p piece.
How many pence do you have in all?

D. You have three 5p pieces.
You get two 10p pieces.
How many pence do you have in all?

A visit to Earth

Princess Plus visits you for a day.
How much will you spend?

hamburger
75p

chips
35p

ice cream
50p

popcorn
30p

hot dog
54p

Coke
20p

chocolate
18p

Fill in the right amounts. Find the answer.

A.

Lunch:

    Princess Plus had:

        hamburger   _____p

        Coke   + _____p

How much in all?   _____p

B.

Cinema:

    Princess Plus had:

        ice cream   _____p

    You had:

        chocolate   + _____p

What is the sum?   _____p

C.

Snack:

    You had:

        popcorn   _____p

    Princess Plus had:

        chocolate   + _____p

Find the total.   _____p

D.

Dinner:

    You had:

        hot dog   _____p

        chips   + _____p

Find the total.   _____p

Princess Plus and her spaceship

Find the answer.

A. 150 creatures are on the ship.
38 more get on.
How many creatures are on board in all?

$$\begin{array}{r} 150 \\ +\ 38 \\ \hline 188 \end{array}$$ creatures

B. The Princess brought 30 helpers.
140 more were brought by the captain.
How many helpers were on board?

_____ helpers

C. 264 Earth people got on at Planet X.
525 Earth people got on at Planet Z.
How many got on in all?

_____ Earth people

D. The ship had room for 227 big robots.
771 smaller robots could also be carried.
How many robots could go in all?

_____ robots

Break the code

The spaceship gets a message in code from a friendly planet. Help the astronauts break the code.

```
tens | ones
  1  |  9         1 9  Comets
+ 1  |  3       + 1 3  Comets
  3  |  2       C  32  Comets
```

I remembered to regroup.

Add. Find the answer to work the code. Write the letter beside your answer in the matching space.

```
  19 comets              37 moons
+ 13 comets           + 14 moons
C  32  comets        M        moons
```

```
  54 orbiters          425 new robots
+ 29 orbiters        + 417 new robots
O        orbiters    N          new robots
```

```
  262 spaceships       145 Earth people
+ 128 spaceships     +  76 Earth people
S          spaceships E          Earth people
```

C			
32	83	51	221

390	83	83	842 !

13

King Minus goes shopping

Subtract the ones.
Subtract the tens.
Subtract the hundreds.

£764   £975   space buggy   £345

How much more does the rocket cost than the robot?

£204   £112

🔺 Subtract.

A.

The king had
£978.   £978

He bought a
computer.   −   £204

How much was
left?   £774

B.

Then the king
had £774.   £774

He also bought a
radio.   _____

Then how much
did he have left?   _____

C.

The king looked
at a rocket.   _____

The king looked
at a space buggy.   _____

How much more
is the rocket?   _____

D.

The king looked
at a robot.   _____

How much more is
it than the radio?   _____

                         _____

14

Subtracting in space

62 creatures are on Earth.
13 are going back home.
How many will be left?

$$\begin{array}{r} \overset{5\ 12}{\cancel{6}\cancel{2}} \\ -\ 1\ 3 \\ \hline 4\ 9 \end{array}$$

You must regroup.

Find the answer to the problem. Then find the sticker with the matching answer. Put the stickers in place on the bottom of the page. What do you see?

A. 33 creatures are on Planet Green.

16 visit Planet Red.

How many are left?

$$\begin{array}{r} \overset{2\ 13}{\cancel{3}\cancel{3}} \\ -\ \boxed{16} \\ \hline \boxed{} \end{array}$$

B. King Minus needs 46 robots.

He has 38 robots.

How many more does he need?

$\boxed{}$
$-\ \boxed{}$
$\boxed{}$

C. 55 creatures are at the space station.

27 creatures are on Planet Red.

How many more are at the space station?

$\boxed{}$
$-\ \boxed{}$
$\boxed{}$

D. 70 spaceships are on Planet Green.

11 spaceships need repairs.

How many are ready to go?

$\boxed{}$
$-\ \boxed{}$
$\boxed{}$

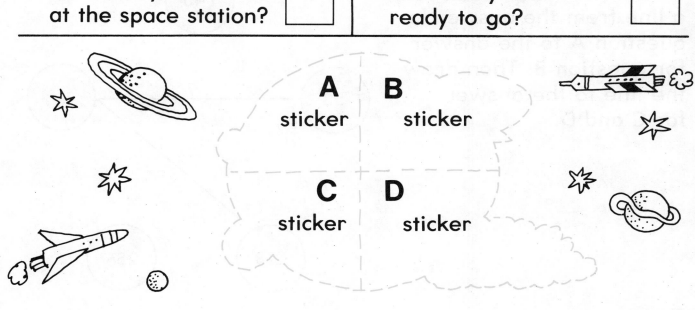

A
sticker

B
sticker

C
sticker

D
sticker

Star journeys

◀ Find the answer.

A. It takes 354 days to get to the Purple Star.

It takes 136 days to get to the Green Star.

How much longer does it take to get to the Purple Star?

$$\begin{array}{r} 3\overset{4}{5}\overset{14}{4} \\ -\ 136 \\ \hline 218\ \text{days} \end{array}$$

_____

B. It takes 528 days to travel to the comet.

It takes 385 days to travel to the Milky Way.

How much longer does it take to travel to the comet?

_____

C. It takes 435 days to reach the Great Red Star.

It takes 179 days to reach the Big Blue Star.

How much longer does it take to reach the Great Red Star? _____

D. It takes 541 hours to get to the Dwarf Star.

It takes 488 hours to get to the Giant Star.

How much longer does it take to get to the Dwarf Star? _____

To find the Giant Star, draw a line from the answer for question A to the answer for question B. Then draw the line to the answer for C and D.

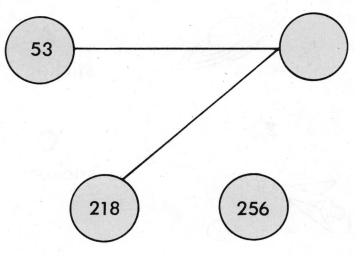

Solving Problems

page q

q

15

5

3

page 8

Press out stickers, moisten, and place them on the pages where they belong.

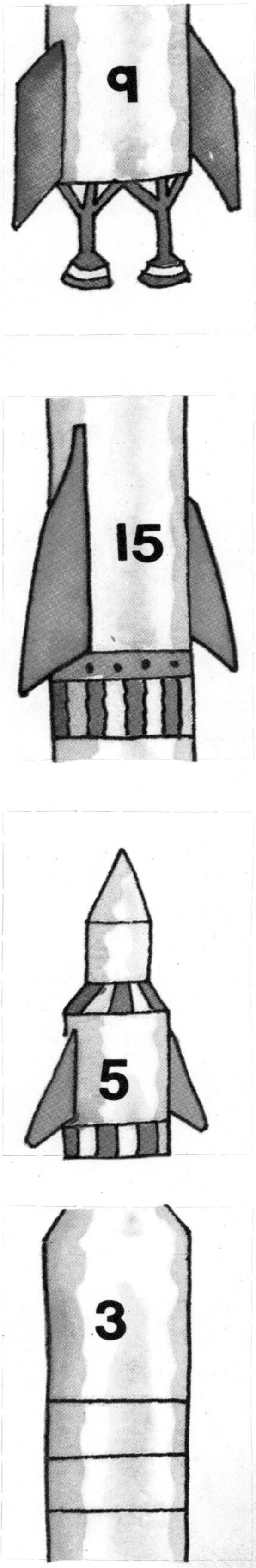

28

17

8

5q

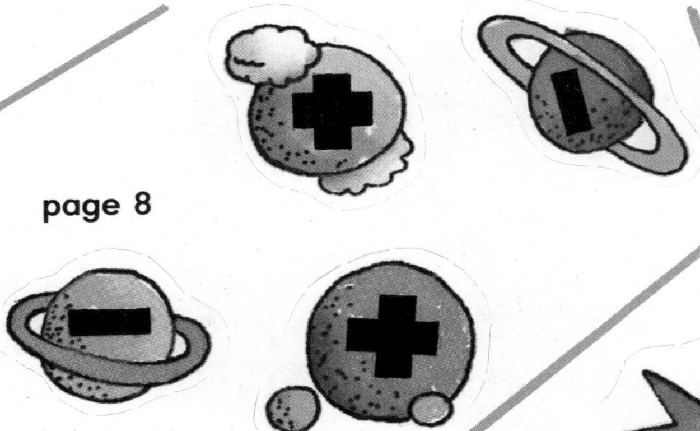

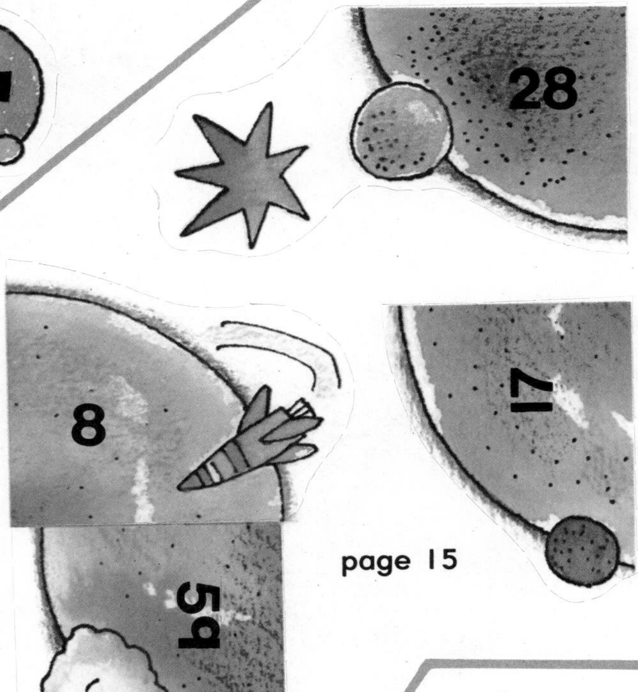

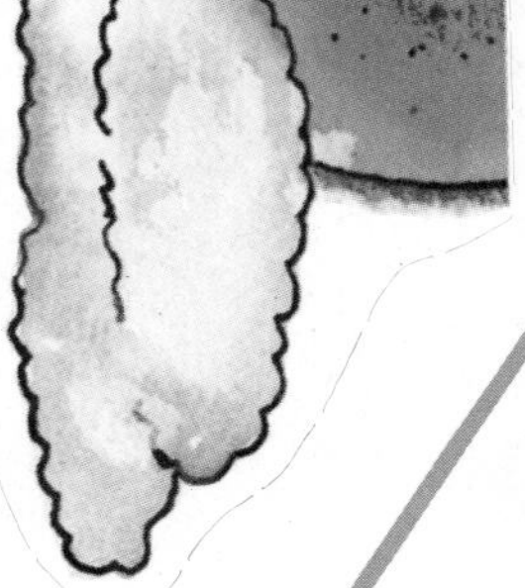

page 15

page 22

Rewards!

page 17

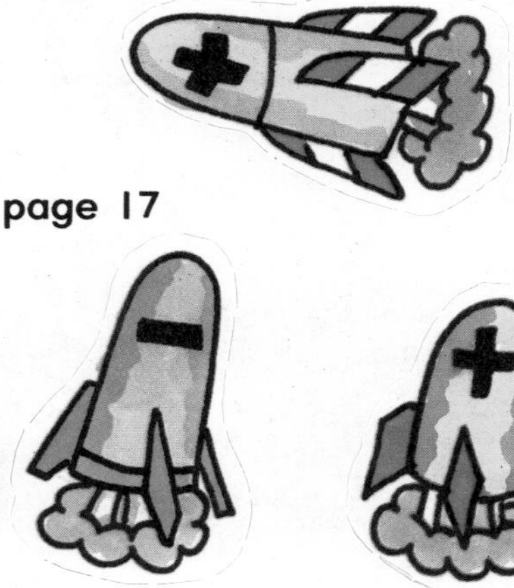

page 23

Use the reward stickers as extra stickers on any page.

More Rewards!

page 20

smaller

smaller

larger

SUPER STAR

BLAST OFF!

FLYING COLOURS!

Sensational!

A party in space

Princess Plus and King Minus decided to get together and give a big party. They invited all their friends.

Read each problem and decide if you need to add or subtract. Find the two plus (+) stickers and one minus (−) sticker. Place the right sticker with each problem. Find the answer.

Problem	+ or −	Answer
A. 6 astronauts came in 1 spaceship. 5 came in another. How many astronauts came in both ships?	sticker	6 +5 —— 11 astronauts
B. It took the astronauts 943 hours to get to the party. It took the robots only 627 hours to get there. How many more hours did it take the astronauts to get there?	sticker	————
C. 11 astronauts, 63 creatures, 35 robots, and 22 pets came to the party. How many guests were there in all?	sticker	————

Fairyland . . .

Jack sold a cow for £10 and bought a bag of beans for £7. There were 125 beans in the bag. How much money did Jack have left?

This problem has too many numbers. You do not need to know how many beans were in the bag.   £10 − £7 = £3

Put an X on the number that is not needed in the problem. Then solve the problem.

A. Jack climbed 273 metres up the beanstalk. Then he climbed another 422 metres. The beanstalk was 888 metres high. How far did Jack climb?

B. The giant was 20 metres tall. He had a bag of gold worth £100. Jack was only 1 metre high. How much taller was the giant than Jack?

C. The giant climbed 451 metres down the 888 metre beanstalk. Then Jack cut the stalk down with 13 axe strokes. The giant fell the rest of the way down. How far did he fall?

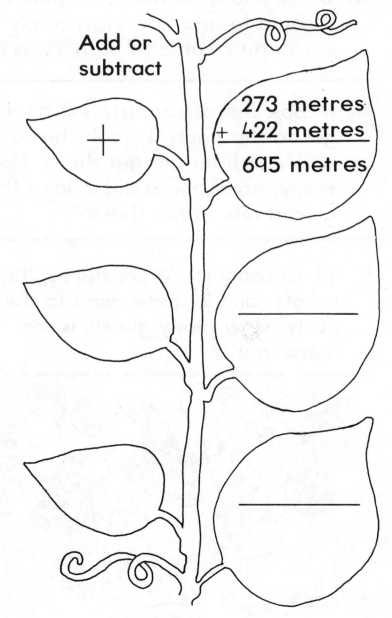

Add or subtract

$$\begin{array}{r} 273 \text{ metres} \\ + \ 422 \text{ metres} \\ \hline 695 \text{ metres} \end{array}$$

Too few numbers

Sleeping Beauty had been asleep for 50 years when the Prince came to the castle. How many more years was the witch's curse supposed to last?

You cannot find the answer because you do not know how long the witch's curse was supposed to last. You need to know that the curse was for 100 years.

Read the story. Look below and colour in the box that gives you the number you need to find the answer. Then find the answer.

A. After Sleeping Beauty had been asleep for 50 years, the tree near the castle had grown to be 117 metres high! How much had it grown since she fell asleep?

The bush was 27 metres high after 50 years.	The tree was 29 metres high when Sleeping Beauty fell asleep.

_____

B. Sleeping Beauty's servants, her 3 dogs, and her 17 cats also fell asleep. How many fell asleep in all?

Hint: Did you remember to count Sleeping Beauty?

The servants were 5 cooks and 3 maids.	The curse was supposed to last for 100 years.

_____

The size of the answer

Sometimes the answer is larger than the largest number in the problem.

This happens when you add.

Sometimes the answer is smaller than the largest number in the problem.

This happens when you subtract.

Read the problem and decide if the answer will be larger or smaller than the largest number in the problem. Find the stickers that say larger and smaller. Place the right sticker with each problem. Find the answer.

Answer

A. Grandmother's house was 7 kilometres away. Little Red Riding Hood had gone 3 kilometres when she met a wolf. How much further was it to Grandmother's house?

sticker

_____

B. Little Red Riding Hood had one hood that cost £9, one that cost £8 and one that cost £2. How much had the hoods cost altogether?

sticker

_____

C. Little Red Riding Hood had 18 sweets in her basket. She gave 8 to her grandmother and kept the rest. How many did she keep?

sticker

_____

20

Using smaller numbers

One day, Hansel and his sister Gretel left the village and wandered through the woods. Along the way, they found a house made of gingerbread.

Hansel scattered 487 crumbs to mark their path. Gretel scattered 479 crumbs. How many in all?

You can see how to solve the problem by thinking of a problem like it that uses small numbers.

Hansel scattered 12 crumbs and Gretel scattered 15. How many in all?

Sometimes a problem seems hard because it has large numbers.

It is easy to see you add to solve this problem.

Think of each problem using smaller numbers. Decide if you need to add or subtract. Then solve the problem with the larger numbers.

A. The witch fed Gretel until she weighed 29 kilograms. The witch fed Hansel until he weighed 38 kilograms. How much more than Gretel did Hansel weigh? _____

B. The witch had 648 sticks of wood. She used 156 of them to build a hot fire. How many sticks of wood were left? _____

C. Hansel brought 368 pieces of gingerbread back to the village. Gretel brought 455 pieces. How Many pieces did they bring in all? _____

Hansel and Gretel's map

Find the stickers for the village, the gingerbread house, and the woodcutter's house. Put them in place. Use the map to work out the problems on the next page.

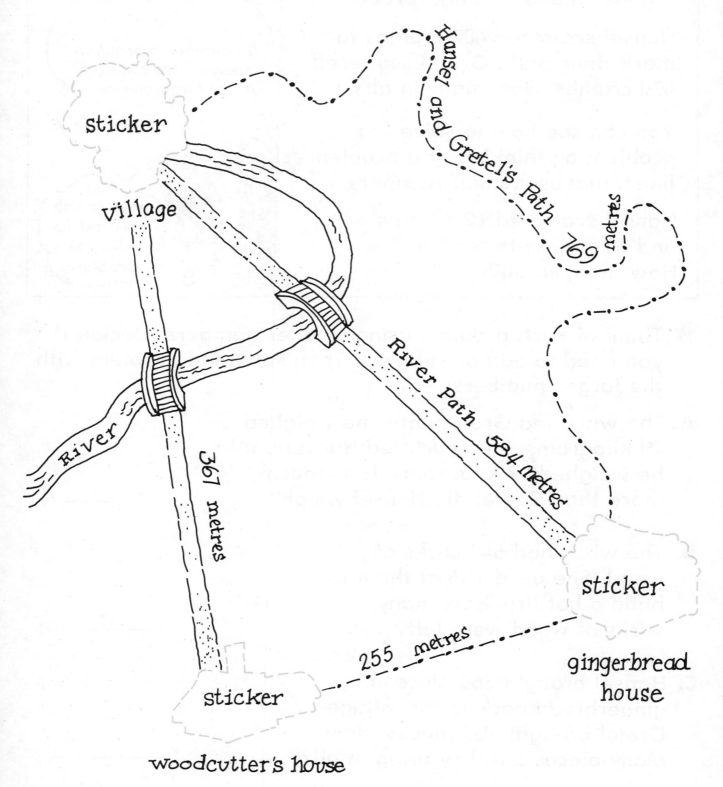

sticker

village

Hansel and Gretel's Path 769 metres

River Path 584 metres

River

367 metres

sticker

gingerbread house

255 metres

sticker

woodcutter's house

Hansel and Gretel's trip

Hansel and Gretel's path to the gingerbread house took them a long way from the village.

Look at the map to see the path that they took.
Read each problem and decide whether you need to add or subtract. Find the two plus (+) stickers and the two minus (−) stickers. Place the right sticker with each problem. Find the answer.

Problem	+ or −	Answer
A. How much further was the path Hansel and Gretel took to the gingerbread house than the River Path?	sticker	$\overset{6\ 16}{7\cancel{6}9}$ − 584 185 metres
B. Hansel and Gretel went to the gingerbread house and then to the woodcutter's. How far did they go in all?	sticker	_____
C. How much further was the village from the gingerbread house than from the woodcutter's house? (Look at the River Path.)	sticker	_____
D. The woodcutter went to the ginger-bread house from his house. Then he took the River Path to the village. How far did he go in all?	sticker	_____

23

Using a graph

Alice's height at different times in her adventure:

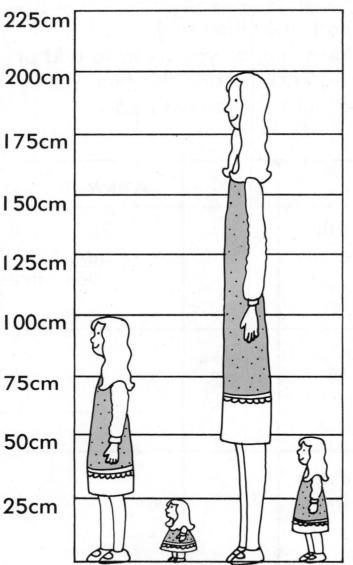

True size

After drinking potion

After eating cake

After eating mushroom

Use the graph to solve the problems below.

A. Alice drank a magic potion from a bottle. How many centimetres did she shrink after drinking the potion? (Hint: She started at her true size before drinking the potion.)

$$\begin{array}{r} 100\text{cm} \\ -\ 25\text{cm} \\ \hline 75\text{cm} \end{array}$$

B. How much taller was Alice than her true size after eating the cake? _____

C. How much shorter was Alice than her true size after she ate the mushroom? _____

D. What was the difference between Alice's size after she ate the mushroom and after she ate the cake? _____

24

Draw a picture

Sometimes you can understand a problem better if you draw a picture. Look at this problem.

Alice went to a land made of squares. Each side of a square was 2 kilometres long. How far was it around 1 square?

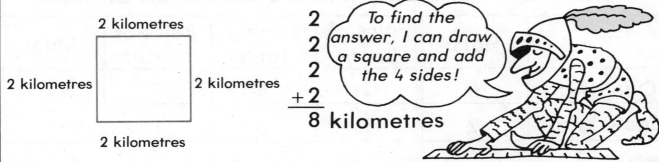

To find the answer, I can draw a square and add the 4 sides!

$$
\begin{array}{r}
2 \\
2 \\
2 \\
+\,2 \\
\hline
8 \\
\end{array}
\text{ kilometres}
$$

First draw a picture for each problem. Then solve the problem.

A. There were rivers that ran between each square. Alice walked from square 1 to square 7. How many rivers did she have to cross?

1	2	3	4	5	6	7

_____ rivers

B. The White King put 6 sticks in a row with 1 metre between each stick. How long was the row?

_____ metres

C. Alice started to read at the very top of page 6. She got sleepy and stopped at the very bottom of page 12. How many pages had she read?

_____ pages

Snow White and the Seven Dwarfs

Sometimes the numbers
you need are in
a table.

The things that Snow White and each dwarf owned:

	Hats	Pairs of Boots	Mining Tools	Pairs of trousers	Mugs
One dwarf	4	2	6	2	1
Snow White	7	1	0	1	1

Use the numbers in this table to solve the problems below.

A. If Snow White washed her own mug and each
of the 7 dwarfs' mugs, how many did she wash?

$$\begin{array}{r} 1 \\ +7 \\ \hline 8 \text{ mugs} \end{array}$$

B. How many more hats did Snow White have
than one of the dwarfs? _____

C. One dwarf polished his boots each week.
How many pairs of boots did he polish in
3 weeks? _____

D. Three of the dwarfs left their tools at the mine
one day. How many tools were left at the mine? _____

You may want
to try multiplication!

Don't forget to label
your answers!

26

Sensible answers

The Wicked Queen's mirror was twice as long as it was wide. It was 75cm wide. How long was it?

Could it be 50cm long? No. It must be longer than it is wide.

Find the answer that makes sense. Shade it in. Then see if you are right by solving the problem.

	Sensible Answer	Real Answer
A. The wishing well was four times as deep as it was across. It was 1 metre across. How deep was it?	1 metre / **4 metres**	_____
B. The dwarfs' cottage was very small. The top of the doorway was 23cm lower than the top of Snow White's head. Snow White was 112cm tall. How tall was the doorway?	89 centimetres / 135 centimetres	_____
C. The dwarfs had worked on their mine for 7 years. Each year they made the mine 3 metres deeper. How deep was the mine?	21 metres / 21 centimetres	_____

Two-part problems

Sometimes there are two parts to a problem. The way to solve such a problem is to work one part and then use the answer to work the next part. Look at this problem.

First Part: Little Pinocchio had been told his nose would grow 8 centimetres each time he lied. His nose was normally 4 centimetres long. After his first lie, how long did it become?

$4 + 8 = 12$ centimetres

Second Part: How long did his nose become after his next lie?

$12 + 8 = 20$ centimetres

Gosh! I don't know why my nose just keeps on growing!

Solve both parts of the problem. You need the answer from the first part to solve the second part.

First Part:
Pinocchio sailed in clear weather for 28 days.
Then on the 5th day of a bad storm the ship sank.
How long was he on the ship?

_____

Second Part:
When the ship sank, Pinocchio was swallowed by a whale. He rode inside the whale for 9 days until he was spat out on shore. How long was he at sea in all?

_____

Which comes first?

Sometimes you will see a problem that you will have to break into two steps to solve. The first job is to find the two problems. The second job is to solve them. Look at this problem.

The Emerald City is exactly in the middle of the Yellow Brick Road. Dorothy started at the beginning of the road and walked 1 kilometre toward the city before the witch stopped her. She still had 2 kilometres to go to get to the city. How long is the road altogether?

First: Find out how many kilometres it is to the city from the point where Dorothy starts.

1 + 2 = 3 kilometres

Land of Oz

Second: You know that Dorothy has to walk half the length of the road. So, the whole road is 2 times as far as she has to walk.

3 + 3 = 6 kilometres

Yellow Brick Road

Emerald City

Decide what the two problems are. Write them down. Find the answer.

There were 4 witches in the land of Oz. 3 of the witches had 2 magic broomsticks each. The fourth had 3 magic broomsticks. How many magic broomsticks were there in all?

First Problem

_____

Second Problem

_____

Two-step problems

Sometimes you have to add *and* subtract to find the answer to a two-step problem. Look at this problem.

3 of the 21 sheep were not in the meadow. But all of Little Boy Blue's 4 cows were in the cornfield. How many sheep and cows were there in all in the meadow and field?

That's easier than finding the missing sheep!

First Step: You have to *subtract* to find the number of sheep in the meadow.

$$\begin{array}{r} 21 \\ -\ 3 \\ \hline 18 \end{array}$$

Second Step: You then have to *add* the number of cows to that answer.

$$\begin{array}{r} 18 \\ +\ 4 \\ \hline 22 \end{array}$$

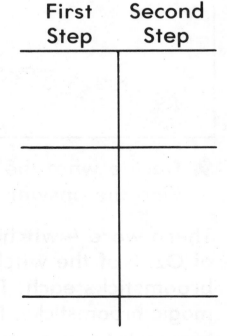

All of these problems have two steps. You have to solve the first step to get the second step. Find the answer.

First Step	Second Step

A. The king had 2 horses and 40 men. 4 of the men were out of the country. How many horses and men were left altogether?

B. Little Bo Peep had 18 sheep. She found 2 black sheep, but then lost 6 white sheep. How many sheep did she have in all?

Answers

Page 1
A. 7
B. 6
C. 5
D. 9

Page 2
A. 6 + 4 = 10
B. 9 + 2 = 11
C. 5 + 3 = 8
D. 7 + 8 = 15

Page 3
A. 10
B. 11
C. 12
D. 16
E. 14
F. 18

Page 4
A. 1 + 2 + 3 = 6
B. 5 + 3 + 4 = 12
C. 3 + 4 + 6 = 13
D. 2 + 6 + 8 = 16

Page 5
A. 6 − 2 = 4
B. 4 − 1 = 3
C. 9 − 5 = 4

Page 6
A. 10 − 6 = 4
B. 6 − 5 = 1
C. 8 − 4 = 4
D. 9 − 2 = 7

Page 7
A. 1 + 2 = 3
B. 2 + 1 = 3
C. 3 + 3 = 6
D. 7 + 4 = 11
E. 7 + 6 = 13
F. 14 + 4 = 18

Page 8
A. 5 (add)
B. 3 (subtract)
C. 5 (subtract)
D. 13 (add)

Page 9
A. 5
B. 3
C. 15
D. 9

Page 10
A. 17p
B. 14p
C. 15p
D. 35p

Page 11
A. 75p + 20p = 95p
B. 50p + 18p = 68p
C. 30p + 18p = 48p
D. 54p + 35p = 89p

Page 12
A. 188 creatures
B. 170 helpers
C. 789 earth people
D. 998 robots

Page 13
C = 32, M = 51, O = 83,
N = 842, S = 390, E = 221
Message: Come soon!

Page 14

A. £ 978
    − 204
    ‾‾‾‾‾
    £ 774

B. £ 774
    − 112
    ‾‾‾‾‾
    £ 662

C. £ 975
    − 764
    ‾‾‾‾‾
    £ 211

D. £ 345
    − 112
    ‾‾‾‾‾
    £ 233

Page 15

A. 33
    − 16
    ‾‾‾
    17

B. 46
    − 38
    ‾‾‾
    8

C. 55
    − 27
    ‾‾‾
    28

D. 70
    − 11
    ‾‾‾
    59

Answers

Page 16
A. 218 days
B. 143 days
C. 256 days
D. 53 hours

Page 17
A. 11 astronauts (add)
B. 316 hours (subtract)
C. 131 guests (add)

Page 18
A. 273 metres + 422 metres = 695 metres
B. 20 metres − 1 metre = 19 metres
C. 888 metres − 451 metres = 437 metres

Page 19
A. 117 metres − 29 metres = 88 metres
B. 3 + 17 + 5 + 3 + 1 = 29 people & pets

Page 20
A. 4 kilometres (smaller)
B. £19 (larger)
C. 10 sweets (smaller)

Page 21
A. 9 kilograms
B. 492 sticks
C. 823 pieces

Page 23
A. 185 metres (subtract)
B. 1,024 metres (add)
C. 217 metres (subtract)
D. 839 metres (add)

Page 24
A. 75cm
B. 100çm
C. 50cm
D. 150cm

Page 25
A. 6 rivers
B. 5 metres
C. 7 pages

Page 26
A. 8 mugs
B. 3 hats
C. 6 pairs of boots
D. 18 tools

Page 27
A. 4 metres
B. 89 centimetres
C. 21 metres

Page 28
33 days, 42 days

Page 29
3 × 2 = 6,
6 + 3 = 9
broomsticks

Page 30
A. 40 − 4 = 36, 36 + 2 = 38
   horses and men
B. 18 + 2 = 20, 20 − 6 = 14 sheep